THE GR
WESTERN CANAL

A BRIEF HISTORY

Helen Harris

Peninsula
Press

First published in 2009 by Peninsula Press,
an imprint of Forest Publishing
Woodstock
Liverton
Newton Abbot
Devon TQ12 6JJ
Republished as a revised and enlarged edition by Peninsula Press in 2014

British Library Cataloguing in Publication Data

A catalogue record for this book is available from the British Library.

ISBN 978–1–872640–59–4 2nd revised and enlarged edition

(ISBN 978–1–872640–58–7 1st edition)

Editorial, design and layout by:
Mike Lang

Typeset by:
Carnaby Typesetting, Torquay, Devon TQ1 1EG

Printed and bound in Great Britain by:
Wotton Printers Limited, Newton Abbot, Devon TQ12 4DZ

Distributed by:
FOGWCbooks@outlook.com

CONTENTS

All photographs by the author unless otherwise stated.

Acknowledgements

I still remember with gratitude help I received from many people during my work on the original editions of *The Grand Western Canal*, whose names are listed in those volumes.

For this abridged version I warmly thank Mike Lang for his valued advice and help in facilitating the production process.

My grateful thanks are further due to Mark Baker, to Denis Dodd and to Philip Brind, also to Robert Hodgson and the Committee of the Friends of the Grand Western Canal for agreeing to co-operate in the book's distribution.

Helen Harris

February 2014

The canal near Tiverton c. 1833. (Drawing by Dudley Weatherley from a picture of an old unidentified painting.)

CHAPTER ONE

Early plans

Ideas for an inland waterway to connect the north and south coasts of England's south-west peninsula had become prevalent by the middle years of the 18th century. Encouraged, no doubt, by the prospects of the Trent & Mersey Canal in northern England (completed 1777), people could see the advantages of a route that would connect the Bristol and English Channels, serving places inland and avoiding hazardous voyages under sail around the stormy seas and rocky coast of Land's End.

Since earlier centuries parts of inland Devon and Somerset had become accessible by waterways from the sea. Exeter had its first canal in 1566 – the first to be built in Britain since the time of the Romans – and, in Somerset, the River Tone had been made navigable for eight miles from its confluence with the Parrett in 1638, and by 1717 the whole way to Taunton. Other proposals for channel-linking routes were considered, including plans for linking the Bristol Channel and River Tamar, which later resulted in the less extensive Bude Canal (opened 1824).

From the mid 18th century to the 'canal mania' years of the 1790s, suggestions were advanced by enthusiastic people for the prospect of providing overland waterway links to connect Exeter and Taunton. Following a meeting of Taunton men in 1768, surveys and reports were requested from a series of engineers. One so commissioned was James Brindley, who sent Robert Whitworth to survey a line. The resulting report of 1769 suggested a lengthy route from Topsham on the Exe estuary (five miles downstream from Exeter) to Cullompton, or from Exeter itself to Cullompton or Tiverton, and on to Wellington and Taunton. Further extension from Taunton to the Bristol Channel was proposed via the Tone Navigation, and a new canal through Bridgwater, serving inland points, to the mouth of the Axe near Weston-super-Mare. However, no immediate action was taken to implement the scheme.

In 1792 a further meeting, towards reviving the idea, was held at Cullompton. This unanimously resolved:

> That the plan for making a navigable canal from Taunton to Topsham with a branch to Tiverton is clearly practicable at a very moderate expense, and that it will be productive of the very greatest advantage to Trade, Commerce and Agriculture.
>
> That among the advantages that may arise from making this canal, appears to

be the easy communication betwixt the Bristol and the British Channel, instead of sailing round the Land's End, which requires various winds, and both in winter and war is a tedious and dangerous navigation.
That this canal will afford a safe, easy and expeditious conveyance for coals, lime, timber, (and other materials for building), iron, cheese, salt, groceries, hardware, wool, etc.
That it is an object of national importance by the ready conveyance of timber to His Majesty's dockyards from the north of Devon, the counties of Somerset, Gloucester, and (particularly) the Forest of Dean, Hereford, Worcester, etc.
That the general communication between Ireland and Scotland with the western part of England and the Bristol Channel would also be rendered much more easy and safe.

Before embarking on the work, while necessary funds were being raised, and typically of the times, alternative advice was sought from other engineers, and John Longbottom, Robert Mylne, and William Jessop were consulted. Jessop recommended omitting the earlier-proposed branches to Cullompton, Tiverton and Wellington, but including a short one to the limestone quarries at Canonsleigh, and suggested siting for a reservoir. He advocated making the canal barge-width, emphasising the importance of accommodating vessels that could cross to south Wales for coal to serve trade at Exeter at favourable prices.

Approval was given to the plan by a meeting of the subscribers and with a resolve to its proceeding. Nevertheless, because of some arising doubts, it was decided to seek the views of yet another engineer, the noted John Rennie, who was currently engineer of the Kennet & Avon Canal, for his opinion and an alternative survey. Rennie surveyed in 1794, considered the proposed route, and produced a plan which included reinstatement of the branches to Cullompton and Tiverton, which Jessop had omitted. Rennie's improved plan was approved at a general meeting of subscribers held on 13 July 1795, with resolve to bring in a Parliamentary Bill for its execution.

By this time anxiety was being felt by citizens of Exeter and voices were being raised. These were on three counts. Firstly, the prospect of the Grand Western Canal was seen as a threat to the city's own Exeter Canal, on which much money had recently been spent in improvements to enable its use by larger vessels for benefiting the city's trade and commerce. Not all the money borrowed for this work had yet been repaid. The carriage of coal on the Exeter Canal formed a considerable proportion of goods carried, and it was felt that profit from this would be jeopardised by a new waterway which could bring Welsh coal more cheaply to Topsham.

Secondly, Exeter feared for its water supply, threatened by construction of reservoirs on the River Culm. The Culm joins the River Exe at Stoke

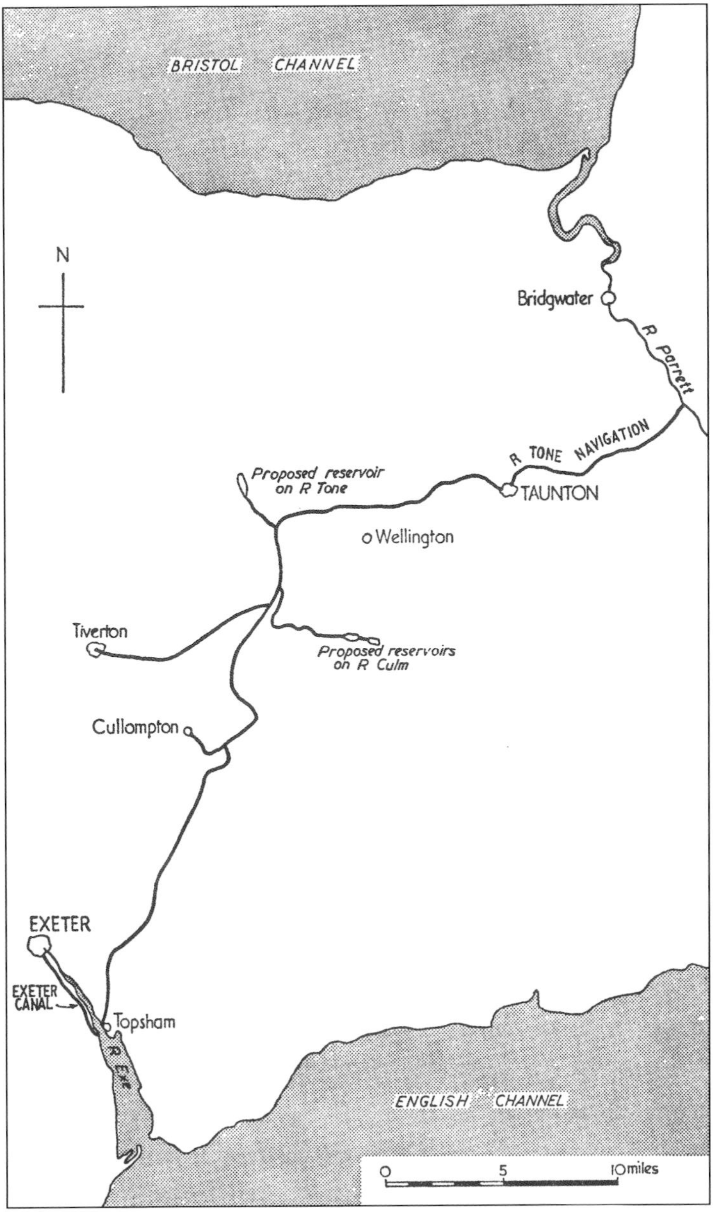

Map showing the approximate route of the proposed Grand Western Canal, from Topsham to Taunton, with branches to Tiverton and Cullompton, as planned by Rennie in 1794.

Canon, and in so doing contributed to the supply vitally needed by Exeter, not only for its domestic requirements, and for powering mills, but as the feeder for the Exeter Canal. And thirdly, the city foresaw a resultant loss in petty dues to which it was entitled by ancient charter on all goods imported into the port of Exeter, which embraced not only the estuary, including Topsham, but also a considerable stretch of the adjacent coastline.

Exeter's opposition was considered carefully by the Grand Western Canal Committee. A change in reservoir siting, avoiding the Culm, was agreed, and other safeguards, and guarantee was offered to the city against loss of dues. Full protection of the rights of Exeter Corporation were assured in the clauses of the Act of 24 March 1796: '... for making a Navigable Canal from the River Exe near the town of Topsham, in the County of Devon, to the River Tone, near the town of Taunton, in the County of Somerset ...' (36 Geo III c.46).

The Act, to which 158 subscribers were listed, ran to 119 clauses, giving details of the canal's route, requirements regarding the taking of land, and other matters. Authorisation was given for the raising of £220,000 in £100 shares, and for a further £110,000 if required.

By this time, however, the country was fully embroiled in the war with France, circumstances made it impracticable for plans to proceed, and prospects for the Grand Western Canal were to remain in the shade for around ten years.

CHAPTER TWO

The first stage of construction

By 1807 there was some revival of interest in prospects for a Grand Western Canal. Raising of the necessary money, however, presented a problem, as many of the original subscribers had died or withdrawn since the 1796 Act. Investigations into matters of finance caused delays, but early in 1810 news was received that a deputation from certain proprietors of the Kennet & Avon Canal had agreed to take over the unappropriated shares. Rennie's Kennet & Avon Canal from Newbury to Bath was by now nearing completion, and there were plans for its extension to Bristol, also for other canals. These facilities, it was foreseen, with the projected Grand Western, would provide a valuable inland waterway from London to Exeter. Time seemed favourable for work on the Grand Western Canal to proceed. A meeting of the committee was held at Taunton to consider the financial position and to decide if construction should start. The importance of a proposed canal connection on to the Bristol Channel was acknowledged, and co-operation offered to a scheme which eventually materialised as the Bridgwater & Taunton Canal. John Rennie was appointed engineer to the Grand Western, twenty-four committee members were named, and measures taken for work to begin.

Decision was taken to commence construction, somewhat oddly, in the middle of the route rather than at either end, and to cut just 2½ miles of the designated main line plus the 9-mile branch to Tiverton. This was in order to make early use of potential trade in lime and limestone from the large quarries at Canonsleigh, in Burlescombe parish, to the farming areas towards Tiverton.

Due ceremony was observed to mark the commencement of the work on 16 April 1810. The *Exeter Flying Post* reported:

> Monday last, pursuant to a resolution of the general meeting of proprietors, held the 12th instant at Cullompton, the great work of the Grand Western Canal was commenced on the summit level in the parish of Holcombe, on land belonging to Peter Bluett Esq., for which occasion the first turf was cut with all due form and ceremony by the Rt Hon Sir George Yonge, Bart, chairman of the meeting, assisted by the lady of John Brown, of Canonsleigh, Esq., who attended for that purpose, in the presence of a numerous body of spectators of all ranks, who testified their joy at the commencement of the work which promises the greatest benefits to the whole country, not without the hope and

prospect of its being the source of still further advantages and improvements. The day being fine, added to the pleasures of the scene. Money and cider were distributed to the populace, while the liberal hospitality of Holcombe Court, to the genteeler sort, closed the scene in a manner suitable to the occasion, and worthy the owners of that respectable mansion.

Operations proceeded under the eye of the appointed superintendent John Thomas, who had overseen building and work on the Kennet & Avon. Doubtless on Rennie's advice, it was decided to cut the summit level 16ft lower than originally planned, to avoid certain difficulties and to obviate the need for locks on the branch, thus saving water. This contributed to the need for a further Act, of 15 June 1811 (51 George III c.168), and greatly increased the cost of excavation and construction. On the credit side, however, various springs of water were found towards the eastern end, near Lowdwells, bubbling up in the newly-cut canal bed, and these, together with some adjacent minor streams, were adequate for the summit level's water requirements, so avoiding the need for reservoirs.

Local people would have watched with guarded interest as work got under way. As the excavation gashed across the countryside, and the thick red mud was carried afield, local people had to adjust to the presence of the navvies, the large number of itinerant workers who came from distant counties to wield picks and shovels according to requirements. Such work and the rough conditions demanded toughness of nature. The men were generally determined in demanding their dues and at times unscrupulous, especially after pay-day and a drinking session. On one occasion a riot occurred at Sampford Peverell due to navvies' grievances. About 300 of the men assembled in the village, causing a general nuisance, with dire results. An inhabitant on whom they centred their wrath, apparently acting in his own defence, fired a loaded pistol, causing one man to die outright. 'Justifiable homicide' was the verdict at the subsequent inquest, but this did not eliminate feelings of distrust.

By the middle of 1811 doubts and difficulties had arisen, due largely to financial problems. The outlook seemed bright as far as plans for other canals were concerned, and the privilege of the Monmouthshire Canal Company to export coal to Bridgwater free of duty had been established, which meant cheaper coal being brought up the River Tone, and enhanced prospects for trade. But the costs of cutting the Grand Western were proving more expensive than expected. The possibility of building the connecting line to Taunton had, as yet, not even been considered, and even continuation of the ongoing construction was in jeopardy. Nevertheless, a report by John Thomas was optimistic in relation to progress and future

The Tiverton basin in 1972, before modern developments. Formerly there were wharves, with the tops of limekilns on the right.

Some of the limekilns below the Tiverton basin (1969), before restoration.

prospects for trade. The main impediment appeared to be the inadequacy of available finance. More than a quarter of the authorised sum for the whole canal had been spent by the summer of 1811 – it appears that high costs having to be paid for land in that time of inflated prices may have been a factor – and there was still much to be done on the work.

Current matters of dissatisfaction and concern within the company were aired at the General Assembly of shareholders held in London on 27 June. The strength of feelings, and uncertainties caused by the continuing war with Napoleon, promoted an atmosphere of caution, and the decision was taken to suspend the works, at least temporarily. Operations therefore came to a standstill, with the excavation reposing as an inconvenient eyesore and most of the navvies doubtless moving on to work elsewhere. In July a sub-committee appointed at the shareholders' meeting made an inspection, and quickly produced a report. It was found that the work so far had been well carried out and progress made, and that certain lengths were nearly finished to an extent that it would be impracticable to leave them in their current state. If suspension was to continue, considerable costs would be involved in securing the suspended works, returning land to former owners, and in payment of compensation to contractors and others. Slow continuation of the works, however, would be financially possible by the collection of arrears on former calls on shares. Optimistic estimates of likely income from the sales of lime and coal that could be carried on the line to Tiverton were noted. With the rates per ton stated in the Act of 1796 for such carriage now being considered below a fair rate, it was recommended that toll rates should be raised to an appropriate level. The report was favourably received and construction work was resumed. A further Act of Parliament was necessary to authorise the increased rates for tonnage, and some small amendments, and this was passed on 20 March 1812 (52 Geo III c.16).

It would appear that by now the hopelessness of ever completing the canal to its originally intended full extent was acknowledged, and the decision made to confine the project to the summit level under construction and its eventual extension to Taunton.

As work resumed and continued, the canal company in 1813 appointed Joseph Champney to carry out a thorough examination of all accounts of expenditure on the undertaking since 1810. Champney's report, presented in September that year, indicated inefficiencies in the keeping of the books, anticipation of credit payments, and failure to record all details. He recommended a proper system of debits and credits. His schedule of expenditure so far showed that this had been heavy:

	£	s	d
Contracts, materials, labour and surveying	87,779	4	8
Land	29,634	10	11
Shares in the River Tone	1,050	0	0
Damages to land etc.	2,301	14	7
Stationery, printing, advertising, stamps, postages and petty expenditure	458	15	6
Law charges	1,510	10	9
Salaries to persons having held or now holding employ under the company	3,376	8	10
Remunerations and presents	765	0	0
Rent, taxes, coals, furniture and sundries, for accountant's house and office	467	12	2
Charges for committees	410	5	3
Sundries not before enumerated	1,070	2	3
	128,824	4	11

Twin culverts which carry a stream through the canal embankment near Burlescombe.

South portal of Waytown tunnel by which the canal passes deep beneath the Wellington-Holcombe Rogus road. Remains of haulage chains on left.

The high embankment on which the canal is carried north-east of Halberton village.

In September 1813 the engineer John Rennie travelled to Devon to view the state of work on the canal. His report gives a good impression of the developing scene along the length of the construction and an idea of the problems having to be dealt with. For convenience, the line from Lowdwells to Tiverton was divided into 'lots'. The first lot, at the eastern end, had, he stated, been very expensive, due to the depths of cutting necessary and the rocky nature of the ground. Careful management of the natural springs was necessary to avoid flooding of neighbouring land, while keeping the channel watered to enable the boating-out of earth produced from the cutting. Masonry work had been well executed, but one bridge was still to be built, also an aqueduct to carry the Whipcott Brook across the canal.

The second lot westwards, at Canonsleigh, was almost finished and contained water, and the third, at Ashford, had reached a similar stage. The fourth (Sampford) lot was less advanced, with several works still to be done.

The fifth, or Halberton, lot had been the most difficult and expensive. With the village of Halberton standing on the line where it would have been logical for the canal to be cut, it had been necessary to adopt an avoiding route that required several pieces of high and expensive cutting – through hard rock and porous sand – to the north of the village. The cut length had had to be lined with clay puddle, causing great delays, and there was still much to be done and several bridges to be built.

The sixth lot, west of Halberton, was also proving expensive, as was the seventh, due to the open and porous nature of the soil and the need for the channel to be fully lined. The eighth and ninth lots also needed lining, but puddle material was here more conveniently available. All these lots nearing Tiverton still required masonry work.

While acknowledging the amount of work still to be done, and the estimated cost of completion, Rennie had great hopes that what was now estimated would suffice, and he concluded his report:

> The Works now appear to me to be in a fair state for completion, and I think with due exertion, the Canal may be opened as far as is now under execution, namely, eleven miles, by the month of September next, and gives me much pleasure to state that the Works, so far as executed, are in general very well done.

During the remaining months of 1813 and into 1814 the work on the canal continued. On 16 June 1814 members of the committee travelled in barges over the embankment at Canonsleigh and it was reported that, despite the unprecedented severity of the weather, the canal should be navigable by the end of August. Two sections at the Tiverton end were still unfinished, with some cutting and puddling yet to be done. Wharves had been constructed at Sampford Peverell, Whipcott, and Halberton, and those at Tiverton were in preparation.

On 25 August 1814 the first barge to travel the length of the canal arrived at Tiverton laden with coal. This promptly resulted in a reduction in the price of coal in the town. The advantage to Tiverton inhabitants had, however, been at high cost to the canal company. The expense of the construction of the canal's first section – involving as it had further raising of calls on shares – had amounted to £244,505 – far exceeding the 1796 estimate for the whole projected canal.

Rock wharf and bridge in 1972.

CHAPTER THREE

Schemes for extension

Although the canal was navigable by the late summer of 1814, finishing was still required and a few months elapsed before trade was fully established. A meeting for the making of by-laws was arranged for January 1815, by which time the sale of lime from Tiverton wharf was being advertised. A busy trade in lime and roadstone soon developed along the waterway from the quarries in Holcombe Rogus and Burlescombe parishes, particularly Canonsleigh, close to the village of Westleigh. It is possible to picture the scene that was appearing at the Tiverton basin. Boats would be arriving with their loads of lime and stone, and horses and carts coming to collect supplies. Soon, or within a few years, the first of the limekilns would have been under construction (there were 14 here by 1842). The elevation of the canal and the lower adjacent ground made it possible for kilns to be built into the basin's retaining structure, with their tops at canal level close to the water's edge. Coal and limestone alternately could then be conveniently tipped into the tops of the kilns, and the burnt lime later extracted from them in the yard below.

While the new venture was no doubt impressive to observe, the trade was far short of the promoters' expectations and nowhere near earlier optimistic estimates. No coal or other anticipated goods were being carried on the canal, and despite efforts to create a trade in coal brought over land from Taunton, to the canal at Lowdwells, this proved no cheaper than land carriage straight through. The need for completion of the canal to Taunton became increasingly apparent.

A difficulty which had to be overcome in considering extension of the canal to Taunton concerned the topography of the countryside from Somerset into Devon and the changes of altitude involved. An ascent of no fewer than 262ft had to be negotiated from the River Tone at Taunton to the canal's summit level at Lowdwells. How this might be achieved was soon occupying the thoughts of aspiring engineers and others.

One engineer who put forward a plan was Benjamin Bevan, in October 1818. His proposal was for a waterway with 30 small locks, and he estimated the total cost – including land purchase, cutting and structure - at £95,000. The plan, together with the estimates of sums likely to be raised by an extended range of materials expected to be carried, was considered by the canal's General Assembly, in 1819. The committee had optimistically modified and contracted individual items of the scheme, thus reducing the

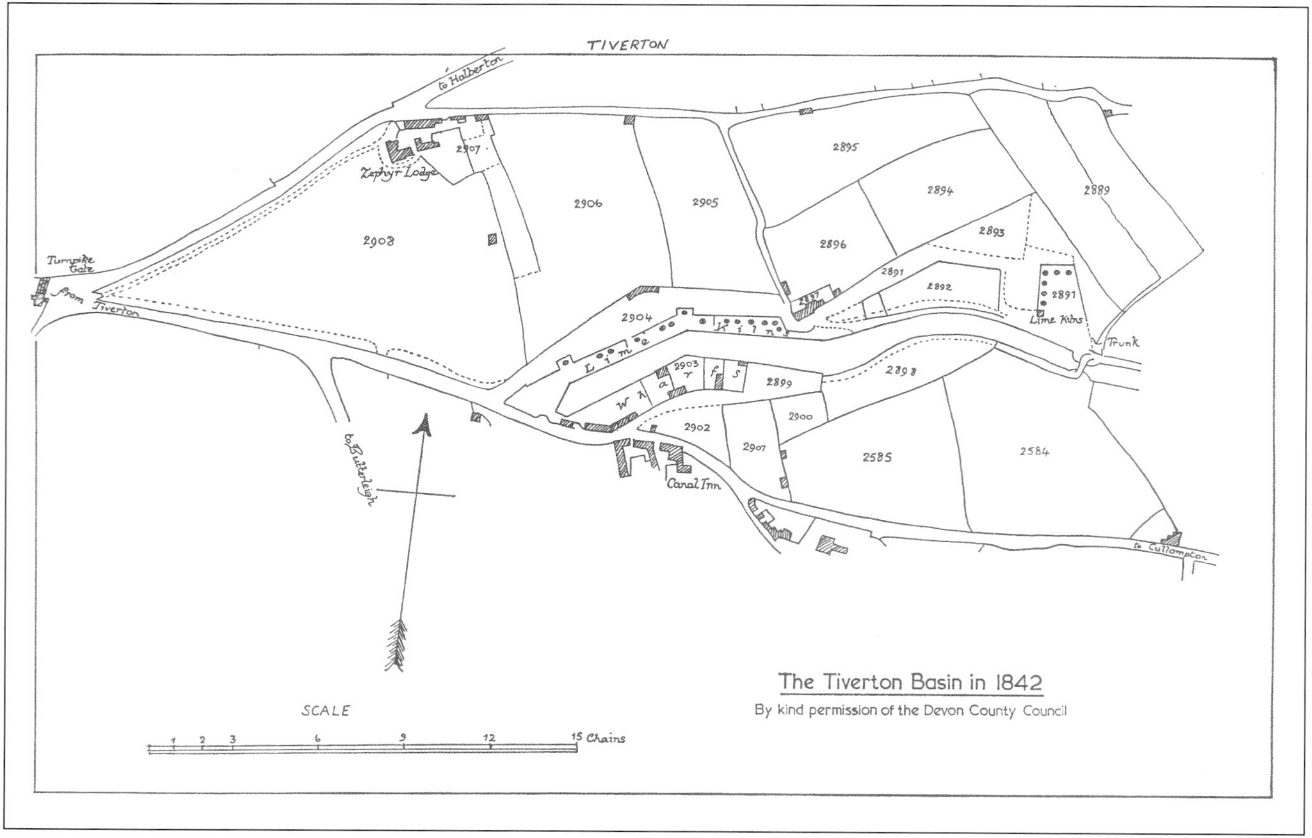

The Tiverton basin in 1842.

estimate to £70,000, but after taking into account the company's available resources, it was decided that the project would be financially impracticable at this time.

In 1822 interest was revived for a Bristol & Taunton Canal, which had been planned early in the century and for which an Act had been obtained in 1811. No start had been made, but the Bristol & Taunton Company foresaw advantages if just the western section could be built – from Taunton to the River Parrett at Huntworth – as an improved alternative to the navigation of the River Tone. Despite petitioning from the Conservators of the River Tone, who had feared competition, a fresh Act was obtained in 1824 and the name of the company changed to the Bridgwater & Taunton

Remains of Lowdwells lock in 1972.

Company. At this stage the Bridgwater & Taunton Company approached the Grand Western Company about the continuation by the GWC of its line to Taunton, or of allowing the B&T Company to construct a linking section. No decision was immediately taken, however, largely due to an alternative proposal for a Ship Canal to connect the Bristol and English Channels, crossing Somerset and east Devon. Heated opposition followed, not least from the Grand Western Canal Company, which feared loss of the advantages offered by a link with the Bridgwater & Taunton, and over the high tolls – prohibitive to any connection – which the Ship Canal was proposing. Nevertheless, an Act for the Ship Canal was passed in 1825, and subscriptions raised, but for various reasons interest waned, and after 1828, by which time (1827) the Bridgwater & Taunton Canal had been completed, the scheme was dropped.

Although amounts received in tolls after the Grand Western's opening fell far short of earlier expectations, with no profits to shareholders, accounts showed a modest but gradually increasing credit balance. By this time, with the failure of the lime trade to reach anticipated volume, it was seen that any chance of future success lay in the continuation of the route to Taunton and connection with the Bridgwater & Taunton Canal.

It was at this point that the engineer James Green made his entry on the Grand Western scene. Green, aged 48, the son of a Birmingham engineer, had shown great talents. He had worked under Rennie in different parts of the country, and in 1808 had come to Devon, initially as the county's Bridge Surveyor, and from 1818-41 as Surveyor of Bridges and Buildings for Devon. Besides his official duties he undertook private work (as was customary at that time), including commitments with canal building. He was adept in the construction of canals in the south-west's hilly countryside, advocating small tub-boats and ingenious methods of lifting. In 1818 he had reported to subscribers of the Bude Canal, and subsequently supervised its construction, involving 5-ton tub-boats and water-powered inclined planes.

In 1829, aware of the Grand Western position, he prevailed on some of the subscribers to consider a plan he was proposing for providing connection on to Taunton. He first considered two alternatives: a railway, or a canal. A railway, he found would have to be very roundabout, needing expensive cuttings and embankments and with steep ascents needing stationary engines for which coal would be costly so far from coalfields. He suggested a small canal, to carry 5-ton boats, with two, or three, inclined planes, and estimated the cost at £50,000. In 1830 James Green proposed a second report, having altered his ideas regarding lifting. He now proposed just one inclined plane, and in addition seven perpendicular lifts, with 8-ton boats being carried. The cost he now estimated at just over £61,000.

A special assembly of proprietors was held on 13 April and the plans examined and discussed. Approval was given and the committee was authorised and instructed to put into effect the 'proper execution' of the work, with the greatest economy, and keeping the sum within £65,000.

CHAPTER FOUR

The second stage of construction

General optimism followed the unanimous agreement on James Green's report. The committee considered that the scheme should produce a good return on capital, and a series of calls on shares were made. Before the end of 1830 plans for the commencement of the work were proceeding and tenders being invited.

At this time the Bridgwater & Taunton Canal Company and the Conservators of the River Tone were in dispute regarding their connection at Taunton, and litigation was in progress. The Grand Western Canal Company felt its position would be more secure if it were to connect directly with the Bridgwater & Taunton Canal rather than with the river, in a deviation of the parliamentary line defined in 1796. This was made possible by agreements and land purchase.

Work soon commenced, and by the middle of 1832 Green was able to report that a considerable part of the work had been done. The line was divided into lots, numbered 1 to 8 from the connection with the Bridgwater & Taunton Canal at Taunton, to Lowdwells, the junction with the already established summit level. Lots 1-3 were being constructed by Houghton & Co, and 4-8 by H. MacIntosh. Much of the cutting had been completed, bridge building was well advanced and awaiting ironwork, culverts were being laid. The viaduct over the Kingston road at Taunton was nearly complete. The connecting lock at Lowdwells was finished. Work in constructing the lifts and inclined plane was in progress. Green concluded his report: 'It may be right for me to state that as far as the several works have proceeded, they have been done in a very efficient manner'.

The perpendicular lifts were a notable feature of the extended length of the Grand Western Canal. The idea for them was not completely new. In a paper which he had contributed to the *Transactions* of the Institution of Civil Engineers (Vol. 2, 1838) James Green explained that the originator was a Dr James Anderson of Edinburgh, who had published a paper on the subject around 1796. Subsequently the use of lifts had been considered for the Bude Canal, and in the construction of the Dorset & Somerset Canal. One had been built for the Somersetshire Coal Canal but deemed unsuitable. Trials were carried out on a lift at Ruabon, on the Ellesmere Canal, another was invented, but decided against, for the Worcester & Birmingham, and an experimental one was built on the Regent's Canal at Camden Town. But none of these went into commercial service and no others were suggested until Green proposed them for the Grand Western in his report of 1830.

Each of Green's seven lifts (when they were eventually completed after much difficulty) consisted of a pair of caissons (or cradles) suspended from carrying wheels and containing water, into which the boats were floated. Power was provided by a preponderating quantity of water added to the descending caisson. They were designed for boats of 8 tons, 26ft long and $6^1/_2$ ft wide.

Green emphasised that the essential requirements for lifts were strength of material, and proper arrangement of the construction. The advantages he enumerated as: firstly, economy in construction costs compared with locks; secondly, the saving of time in passing boats from one level of canal to another; and thirdly, the small consumption of water compared with locks.

As with the first length of the canal, building of this second length did not proceed as quickly or as smoothly as had been hoped. The committee's report of 1833 noted 'regular and progressive executions of the work', and enquiries received about wharves and boats. But there had been delays, although no blame was directed at the engineer or contractors. The work was simply taking longer than expected. One cause was the realised necessity for a lock at the foot of the first lift at Taunton, in order to secure a uniform level of water near the junction with the basin of the Bridgwater & Taunton Canal. Others involved unforeseen problems with cutting and earth moving, agreements with some landowners requiring provision of additional bridges or buildings, and other unexpected necessary work along the canal's course.

By 1834 the delays and extra work, and higher land prices, were having financial effects. Green had found it necessary to overspend on contracts, money had to be borrowed through mortgages from various individuals, and interest on it paid out of revenue from the summit level. In February 1835 it was reported that the canal was navigable from Taunton to Bradford, near Wellington, and had been used by barges carrying coal. But farther along the route, obstacles were encountered in building the remaining lifts, requiring modifications which Green had had to make at his own expense, but with inconvenience to the company. Also, the inclined plane was not functioning. The canal company had become increasingly dissatisfied with its engineer, and early in 1836 James Green was dismissed.

Facing page and overleaf: Drawings of perpendicular lifts reproduced from James Green's 'Description of the Perpendicular Lifts for passing boats from one level of canal to another, as erected on the Grand Western Canal' in the *Transactions* of the Institution of Civil Engineers, Vol 2, 1838.

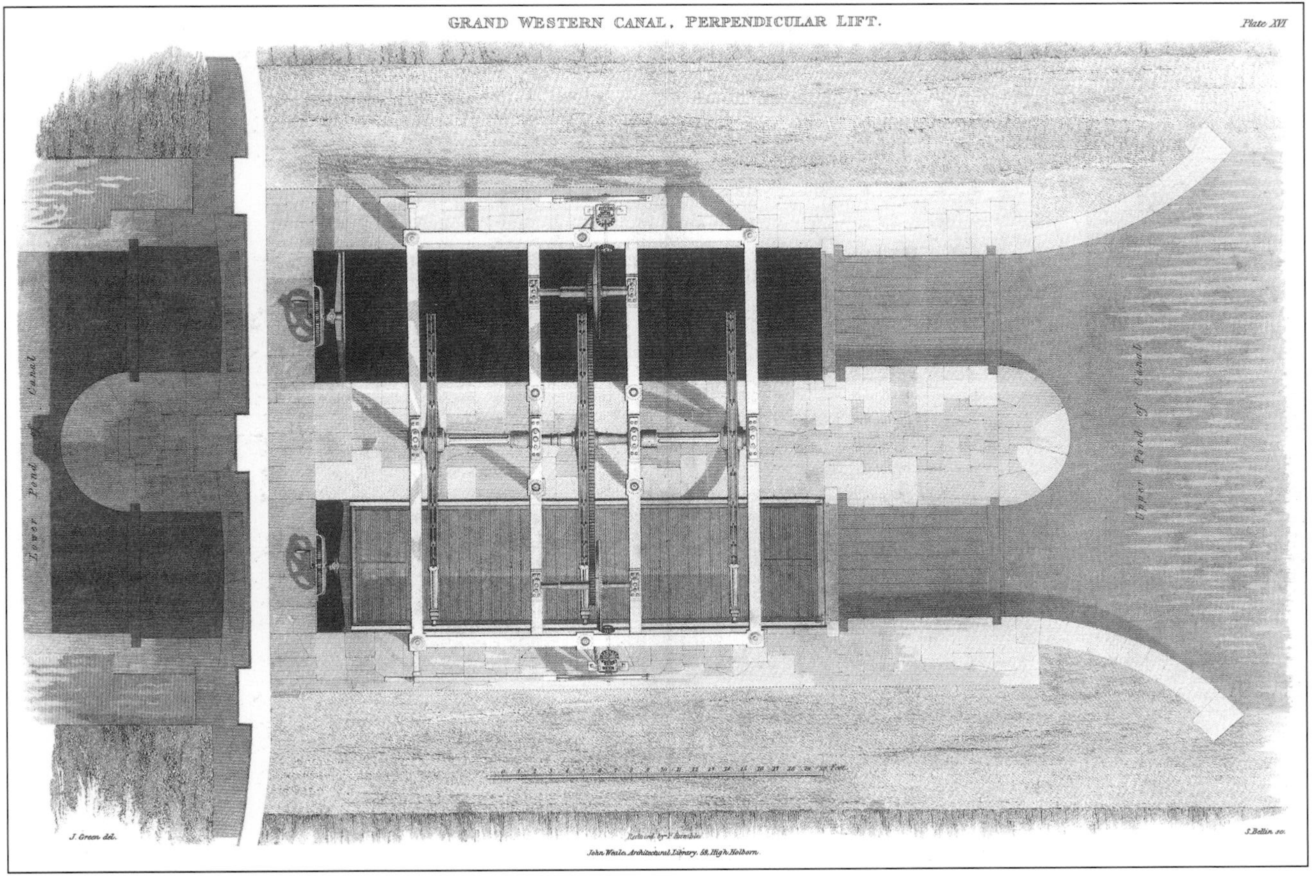
GRAND WESTERN CANAL, PERPENDICULAR LIFT.
Plate XVI
Lower Pond
Canal
Upper Pond of Canal
0 1 2 3 4 5 6 7 8 9 10 11 12 13 14 15 16 17 18 19 20 Feet.
J. Green del.
S. Bellin sc.
John Weale, Architectural Library, 59, High Holborn.

J. Green del.

Reduced by F. Rumble

S. Bellin sc

John Weale, Architectural Library, 59, High Holborn.

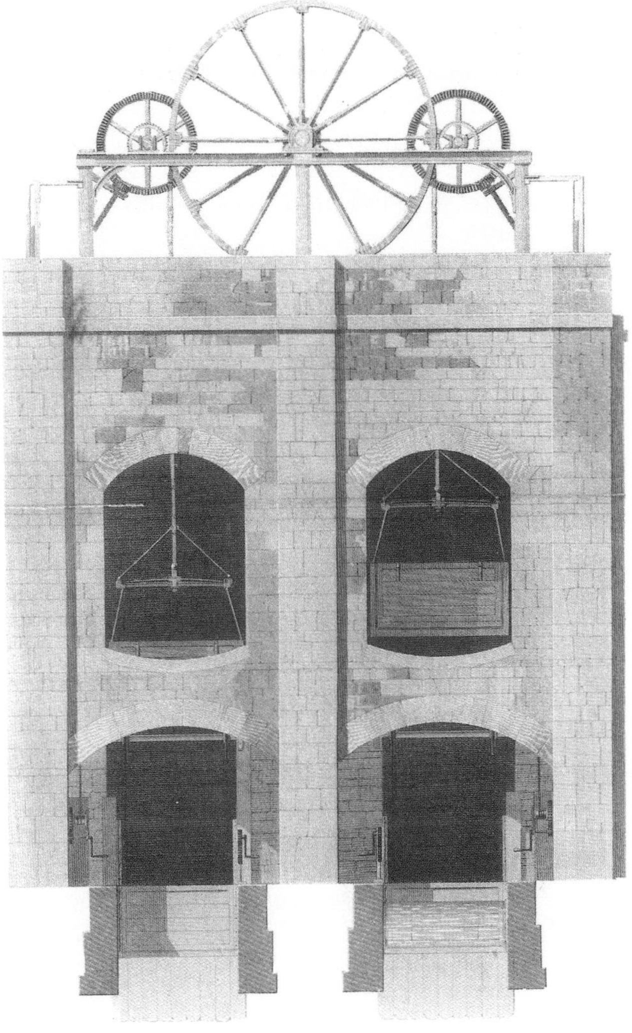

TRANSVERSE SECTIONAL VIEW

0 1 2 3 4 5 6 7 8 9 10 11 12 13 14 15 16 17 18 19 20 Feet

J. Green del. *Reduced by F. Rumble* *S. Bellin sc.*

John Weale, Architectural Library, 59, High Holborn.

In his place, John Twisden, a retired Royal Navy captain who had been associated with the canal construction since 1829, was retained to supervise the work, and James Easton of Taunton asked to survey the machinery.

The canal company now found itself in a state of some desperation. The canal extension was partially completed, but navigable connection with the summit level could not be achieved because of obstacles in the form of partially built lifts, and an inclined plane that would not work. The locations of the various structures (from east to west), and the rise of level of each were as follows:

LOCKS	Taunton, stop-lock	
(Excluding those forming parts of lifts)	Lowdwells rise $3\frac{1}{2}$ ft to join summit length	
LIFTS	Taunton	rise $23\frac{1}{2}$ ft
	Norton	$12\frac{1}{2}$ ft
	Allerford	19 ft
	Trefusis	$38\frac{1}{2}$ ft
	Nynehead	24 ft
	Winsbeer	18 ft
	Greenham	42 ft
INCLINED PLANE	Wellisford rise 81ft, length 440 ft, gradient approx 1 in $5\frac{1}{2}$.	

In May 1836 the committee requested the engineer W.A. Provis to come from London and visit the canal works from Taunton to the summit level, and to investigate the lifts and inclined plane and the causes of the plane's failure. Provis responded quickly, and on 28 June presented his report. He commenced his inspection at the Taunton end, where he found the condition of the structure generally good. Moving westwards, he noted that the aqueduct which carried the canal over the Taunton-Kingston road had a cast iron trunk for the waterway (as did the other aqueducts), and iron ribs on either side to carry the towpath supported by abutments and wing walls of masonry. Most aqueducts and bridges were composed of masonry – of stone, or stone and brick – generally in the case of road bridges with iron ribs for support. Where it was necessary to keep the road over the canal very low, the towpath was sunk under the bridge to a lower level, with cast iron plates fixed to prevent encroachment of water. The few culverts that passed beneath the canal for irrigation or drainage were generally rough, but sufficient for the purpose. There were public wharves at Taunton,

Silk Mill bridge, which carried the Bishop's Hull-Staplegrove road over the line of the former canal west of Taunton (1972). Now demolished due to road improvements.

The fine ashlar arch of the aqueduct which carried the canal across the former drive to Nynehead Court, near Wellington. Railway arch visible in the distance (1972).

A section of the disused canal south of Norton Fitzwarren, still containing water (1972).

Section of the abandoned canal immediately above the Allerford lift (1972).

Bradford and Payton, belonging to the company and others, private ones, at Bradford, Tonedale and Wellisford.

Considering the lifts, Provis noted that the first three, Taunton, Norton and Allerford, were similar. They were constructed on the early principle of Dr Anderson except that no means were provided for keeping the water in the caisson chambers at a lower level than the water in the canal. This caused difficulties in getting the caisson to sink deep enough to allow the boat to float smoothly into the lower length of canal, and the ascending caisson to rise high enough for its boat to pass easily into the upper one. Locks were provided to correct this and it was said that the lifts had worked reasonably well for two years, apart from slight accidents. The Trefusis lift differed from the previous three in having the gates of the caisson chambers and of the caissons lifting vertically and ingeniously balanced. The lift at Nynehead was similar to Trefusis, although the upper masonry, being built on an artificial embankment, had sunk slightly. The Winsbeer lift was also similar. All these three also had locks. The Greenham lift, the highest, was the only one in which Dr Anderson's principle had been fully carried into effect, having a drain from the bottom of the caisson to draw off water to sufficient depth; consequently the need for a lock was eliminated.

Remains of the Nynehead lift which raised the boats a height of 24ft (1972). (Before recent archaeological investigations and restoration.)

Close-up of the Nynehead lift masonry, showing holes into which the metal framework was bolted (1972).

The new work of the Lowdwells lock, which was capable of raising four boats at once the $3^1/_2$ ft to the summit level, was considered by Provis to be 'an excellent piece of workmanship'.

Provis then turned his attentions to the Wellisford inclined plane, and in order to determine why it would not work he studied it in close detail. Following Green's plan the parallel lines of railway were laid along the slope for carriage of the canal boats, which were floated out of the canal to travel on special cradles fitted with wheels. By means of an endless chain operating above, and short buckling chains attaching the boat to it, an ascending boat would be drawn up, with the descending one providing partial counterbalance. Clearly, additional lifting power was needed to provide for disparity of loads and to overcome friction. Green had planned for this to be provided by means of two iron buckets suspended in an 81ft deep well sited at the top of the plane, which were made to rise and fall alternately, by the weight of 10 tons of water added to the descending bucket. On reaching the bottom of the well a bucket's gravity would force up a valve which allowed water to escape by a drain to the canal's lower pound. However, the system was found not to work suitably even when two empty boats were added to the cradles, and was quite inadequate for use when one was loaded.

Approach channel from east to Nynehead lift (1999) after clearance work.

View down the slope of the former Wellisford inclined plane (1972). The boats travelled on wheeled cradles which ran on rails and were raised 81ft over a distance of 440ft.

In order to see an inclined plane of this type working in service, Provis travelled west to the Devon-Cornwall border, to see the Bude Canal's Hobbacott plane, also designed by Green. Although on the day he visited the great plane was out of action due to a breakdown and was being worked by a stand-by steam engine, he was assured that, in normal circumstances, working was efficient, a boat weighing $5^1/_2$-6 tons being taken up the 225 ft vertical rise in about 3 minutes. Fifteen tons of water in the descending bucket provided the motive power. Cradles were not used at Hobbacott – the boats were fitted with wheels and ran directly on the railways. Considering this, and the relevant figures, it became apparent to Provis that those suggested by Green for Wellisford were impracticable and that 25 tons of water would be required to raise the 8-ton boats, a weight of water which, he considered, was greater than the existing machinery was strong enough to bear.

Before he left the Grand Western, Provis also advised on the canal's water supply, recommending that the waterway should be lined wherever necessary to avoid wastage of the supply from the Lowdwells springs as it passed along to serve the lifts and inclined plane.

The canal's funds had by now been used up, and income was exceeded by current expenses. The superintendent, Captain Twisden, himself advanced over £1,000, and two further engineers, Thomas Maddicks and Isaac Westwood, were engaged to advise on completion. The time was favourable, an Act having been obtained in 1887 by the Bridgwater & Taunton Company for continuation of its canal towards Bridgwater. Further loans were obtained and a steam engine was purchased to work the Wellisford plane. Remaining work on the canal was completed and on 28 June 1838 it was fully opened. The cost of the extension to Taunton had apparently cost approximately £80,000.

How James Green failed in his calculations for the Grand Western Canal's inclined plane is a mystery that will never be solved. He remained Devon County Surveyor until 1841 and did further work on Newport Docks, in Bristol, and on the South Devon Railway, but no more on canals. He died in 1849.

The only other successful canal lift built in Britain has been the Anderton lift between the River Weaver and the Trent & Mersey Canal, opened in 1875 and powered by electricity. Also of interest is the lift-lock on the Severn-Trent Waterway at Peterborough, in Ontario, Canada, which takes larger vessels and works, like those on the Grand Western Canal, by water counterbalance.

CHAPTER FIVE

The coming of the railway

With the Grand Western Canal completed in 1838 (although not to the full extent originally planned), prosperous and more peaceful times must surely have been expected as rightful rewards for the struggle that had been endured and overcome. At a cost of approximately £330,000 the $24^{1}/_{2}$-mile Grand Western Canal was connected at Taunton to the Bridgwater & Taunton Canal, enabling a through water route from the Bristol Channel to Tiverton. Tub-boats could navigate the $13^{1}/_{2}$-mile Taunton-Lowdwells length, the 262ft rise being accomplished by seven lifts and an inclined plane, while barges carrying 40 tons travelled the 11-mile broader summit level from Lowdwells to Tiverton.

A rise in income had, indeed, begun. Even from 1836, when the Taunton section had become navigable as far as Wellington, amounts from tolls had increased, and the figure showed a major jump when the through route to Tiverton was accomplished. They reached a peak in 1844, rising to almost £5,000. Tiverton had become a busy scene of activity. Wharves and kilns were established at the basin, and limekilns were also built close to the quarries at Holcombe Rogus and Burlescombe. Although, yet again, revenue was below hopeful estimates, the trade was welcome locally, and Tiverton traders took full advantage of the new facility. But practically all the traffic was westwards, with only a very small proportion going in the opposite direction, to the company's obvious disadvantage.

Hardly had the canal's rhythm of working become established when a shadow appeared on the horizon. The railway age had taken hold in the country, and in the early 1840s the projected Bristol & Exeter Railway, under its engineer I.K. Brunel, was advancing south-westwards. Authorised by an Act of 1836, the line reached Taunton in 1842, by 1843 had been laid as far as Beam Bridge near the Somerset-Devon border, and in 1844 (following construction of the Whiteball tunnel beneath the county boundary) was completed to Exeter. Moreover, a branch was planned from it to the town of Tiverton, which was completed in 1848.

There was nothing the canal company could do to halt the railway's progress, nevertheless, efforts were made to protect rights where possible. One dispute involved the proposed line of the railway at Trefusis, where the canal was to be crossed at the site of the lift. This led to an interview with Brunel in the hope of re-routing, but little concession resulted and the railway was carried almost directly over the lift's position. Slightly later, the

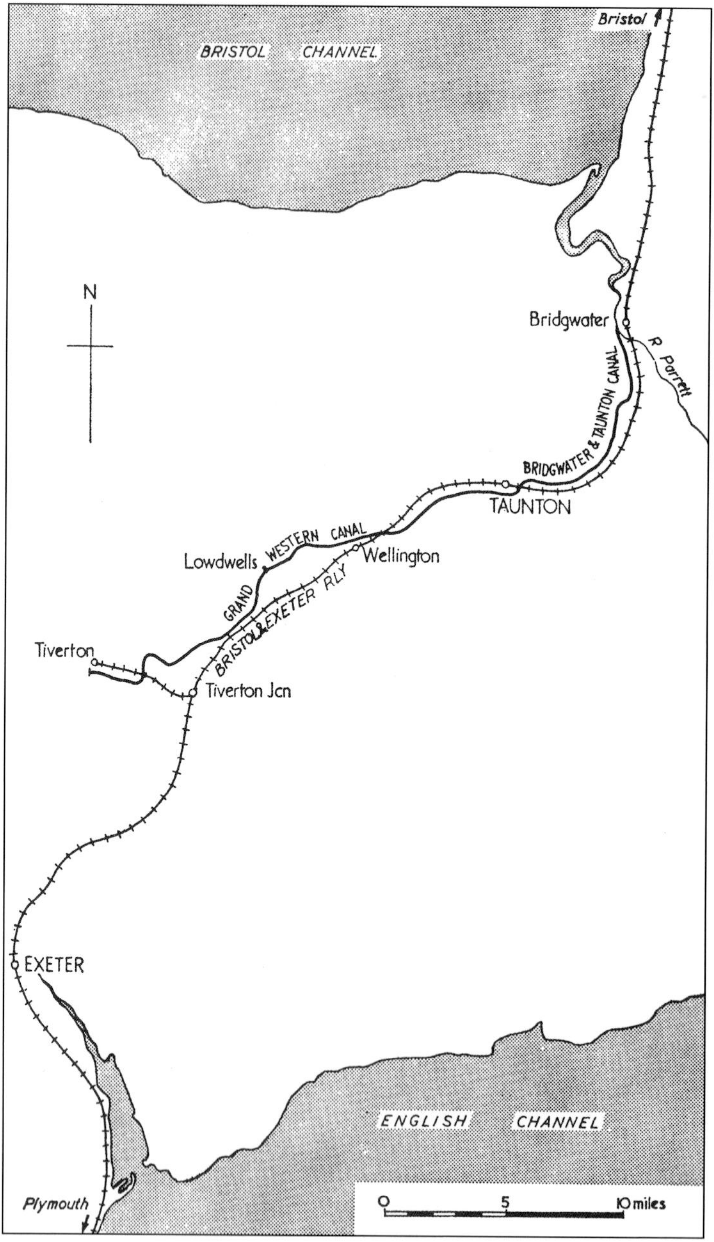

The Grand Western Canal, Bridgwater & Taunton Canal, and the Bristol & Exeter Railway, 1848.

cutting of the railway's Tiverton branch required excavation under the canal near Halberton and the building of an aqueduct to carry the water over it. This caused closure of the canal for two weeks and consequent payment to the canal company of £1,200 for lost trade.

The aqueduct which carried the canal across the former Tiverton Junction-Tiverton branch railway. (Before the aqueduct's restoration.)

It was not only the Grand Western Canal Company that felt great concern about the coming of the railway. The situation was also devastating for the Bridgwater & Taunton Canal Company which in 1841 had completed its extension to the River Parrett at Bridgwater, at great cost. A dock had been built there where canal craft, including Grand Western tub-boats, could load directly from the sea-going vessels. The company immediately lowered its tolls and in 1844 negotiated on toll charges with the Grand Western Company, but in 1845 it became bankrupt and relations between the two companies were strained. The Grand Western Company was suffering its own effects with, after a peak in 1844, a sharp fall in tolls, and was beginning to see its only salvation in some form of agreement with the railway.

Once the railway reached Tiverton, traders opened yards at Tiverton station and used the railway almost exclusively for nearly all goods coming from Taunton and beyond. Reduced quantities of lime and stone remained almost the only traffic on the canal. The Grand Western and Bridgwater &

Taunton companies renewed their alliance in order to cut tolls and fight the competition, but the railway promptly lowered its own rates. Canal tolls were reduced even further, which kept down charges by the railway – resulting in temporarily cheaper coal at Tiverton, doubtless to the joy of the townspeople.

With debts mounting, the Grand Western Company acknowledged the hopelessness of the situation, and in 1853, following the course taken by the Taunton & Bridgwater Company, offered its canal to the railway company for lease or sale. At this stage the railway company was unwilling to buy the canal but was prepared to take a lease. After legal matters had been dealt with, including arrangements with mortgage holders, a meeting of the Grand Western Canal shareholders was held on 10 October 1854 when assent was given to the handing over, retrospectively dated 11 October 1853.

In 1854 the company paid its first dividend to shareholders – the paltry sum of 4 shillings (20p) per £100 share, which was repeated in the remaining years of its existence. Whilst dwindling quarry traffic continued on the summit level, the Lowdwells-Taunton stretch fell into disuse and its structures deteriorated. After ten years the company felt that the time had arrived to seek legal powers for disposing of the canal and an authorising Bill. Some opposition was raised by people on grounds that private or public interest could be affected by closure. Consequently the canal company had to prepare a case in support of the Bill which was presented to a committee of the House of Lords on 25 April 1864. Twelve weeks later, on 14 July 1864, an Act for the sale of the canal to the railway company, and for abandonment of a portion of it, was passed. By it the canal company was empowered to seek to sell the canal and all its property for £30,000. The transfer of the canal from the Grand Western Canal Company to the Bristol & Exeter Railway Company formally came into effect on 13 April 1865.

CHAPTER SIX

Century of twilight

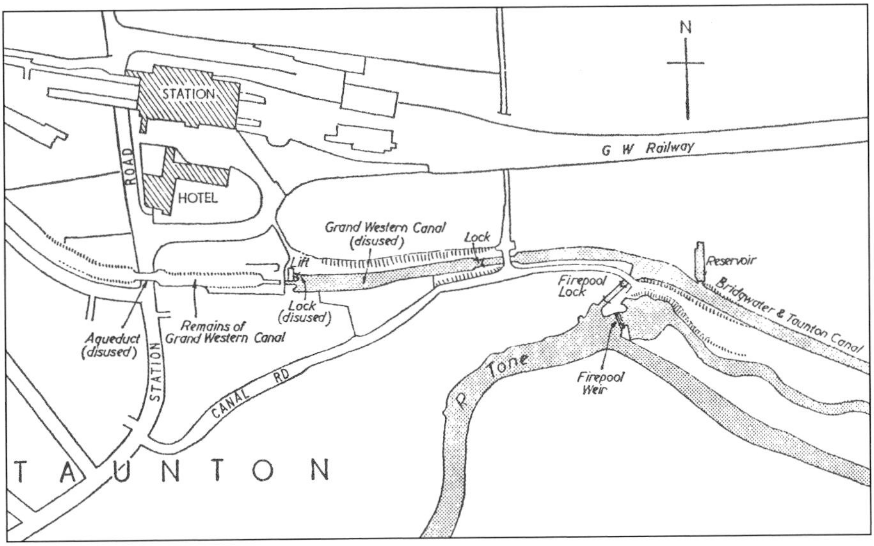

The Grand Western Canal at Taunton. The remains in the 1880s, based on the first edition 25in ordnance survey.

After its acquisition of the Grand Western Canal the Bristol & Exeter Railway Company took steps towards official closure of the Lowdwells-Taunton length, and this took effect in 1867. The lifts and inclined plane were then dismantled and the machinery and structural materials disposed of. The land which the canal had occupied was sold off, mostly to adjacent owners, although a length at the eastern extremity was retained for subsequent expansion of goods yards and sidings at Taunton station. Much of the abandoned length, although absorbed back into farmland and partially levelled, continued to reveal vestiges of the canal's transitory existence, in the form of water-retaining stretches and associated plant life, and changes of level in varying degree, at points where the canal's route had been raised.

The summit level, from Lowdwells to Tiverton, was allowed to survive by virtue of the limestone traffic from the quarries. This trade continued for a further sixty years, to a diminishing extent. From the Westleigh quarries in the Canonsleigh area stone was carried on a half-mile tramway, through a tunnel and along an embankment, to the canal at Fossend wharf, Burlescombe. (A branch of the tramway also crossed the canal on a viaduct to terminate at Burlescombe railway station.) Slightly farther east, shorter tramways conveyed stone from the quarries at Fenacre and Whipcott to the canal – at Whipcott delivered to the waterside by means of a chute. Limestone was also burnt in kilns here, and the resulting lime, as well as stone – like that from Westleigh – carried in boats on the waterway to Tiverton or to small wharves along the way for building and road material.

At Tiverton basin kilns continued in operation at least up to 1895 before being filled in in the early 1900s, and memories survived of boys warming their feet by the fire and sometimes roasting potatoes in the embers.

Following railway amalgamation in 1876, the canal passed into the ownership of the Great Western Railway Company. By 1904 the sole traffic on the canal was roadstone, most of it carried to a crushing depot at Tiverton Road Bridge. This continued until 1924-5, using two boats which worked as a pair, chained together fore and aft, the leading boat having a pointed bow and carrying 8 tons, the follower a box boat carrying 10 tons. Latterly about 7,000 tons were carried annually in this way. The crushed stone was delivered for use in road work across a wide area by a fleet of steam driven traction engines and wagons, whose wheels were often detrimental to road surfaces. (Perhaps appropriately, the firm also owned fourteen steam rollers which were hired to local authorities for road repair work.) It was not at all unusual in those years to see stone-cutting men at work at roadside landing places near the smaller wharves, preparing material for use locally.

The canal provided a medium for other uses in the early part of the 20th century. When the washing of sheep before shearing was still customary in some places, sheep were brought to a point near Fenacre Bridge, put into the canal on one side and taken out on the other, their heads kept above water by means of a special pole. Advance notice had to be given to the railway authority by which a charge was made per score of sheep washed. Charges were also made for any water extracted along the route.

An unusual feature of industry along parts of the canal was the gathering and marketing of water lilies. Rights for this were leased by the railway to a Sampford Peverell family who, in summertime, picked from a boat drawn by a slow-moving horse. The packed blooms were dispatched by rail to London, the Midlands, and the North, with the trade continuing to the mid 1960s.

Various forms of recreation took advantage of facilities offered by the canal, such as boating activities and coarse fishing - from small boys to more serious anglers, with records of pike taken up to 28lb in weight.

When, in very cold winters, the water froze, the skaters would gather. On one occasion three young men skated all the way from Burlescombe to Tiverton; on another it is said that, when a man fell through the ice at Tiverton his lady friend cheerfully called out to him 'Keep cool dear'.

Although at the eastern end the surviving canal soon became impassable to boats due to plant growth, maintenance from the quarries westwards was still required, and a small working gang was employed. No dredging was done, but weeds had to be kept cut (avoiding water lilies) involving a series of knives or saws bolted together and suspended on a rope, with men on either side of the canal holding the rope and working a reciprocating action. The weed was then raked out, dried and burnt. Hedges also had to be kept trim, and the towpath kept in good order.

The section of canal between Halberton and Tiverton (which had caused problems to Rennie in earlier days) was particularly subject to leaks due to a badly fissured bedrock. This caused a fall in water level, needing frequent attentions with clay puddle by the maintenance men. Eventually, in the 1930s, when stone traffic had ceased, the half-mile section in which the leaks occurred was stanked off. The canal's eastern end was thus deprived of the water coming from the Lowdwells springs, and relied solely on land drainage and surface water.

By now, maintenance was kept to a minimum, the canal had become silted, and plant growth had increased. It was still, however, a familiar part of the landscape, providing a pleasant setting for walking and a habitat for wildlife. When, on 1 January 1948, the railways were nationalised, the canal passed from the hands of the Great Western Railway Company to those of the British Transport Commission. In 1962 it was formally closed to navigation, and in January 1964 put under the ownership of the British Waterways Board. For many, after this century of twilight, the eventual sinking of the canal into obscurity seemed inevitable, but it was a twilight that was to see a new dawn.

The stanked-off section near Halberton 1969.

The section after restoration and re-watering, photographed from same viewpoint 1984.

CHAPTER SEVEN

New life

By the 1950s and early 1960s the question of what was to happen to the now seemingly degenerate Grand Western Canal was becoming a matter of local discussion and speculation. Some people wanted it filled in – making it a dump for unwanted ballast and perhaps a basis for a future bypass road for the town. Others thought it should be cleaned out and used for housing. By 1962 a body of opinion had developed which took the view that the canal should be preserved for its amenity value, maintained in good condition and made available for worthwhile projects. A public meeting was held, and a preservation committee formed.

The matter lapsed until 1966 when news was given that the local council's planning committee was recommending infilling by British Waterways Board and the land used for housing. Strong action by one of the councillors, William Authers, and others, against such proposals, and massive public support for its preservation became evident at a public meeting held in September 1966. The matter rumbled on, and another great show of enthusiasm for retaining the canal followed in 1969 when an estimated 1,200 people attended a towpath walk to demonstrate opinion. Such events gave the preservation committee confidence to continue with a sustained campaign. Investigations ensued regarding the canal's restoration and suggested use as a country park, and a management body was set up to handle negotiations. Consequently, after prodigious work, and the sorting out of legal matters, the canal was handed over by British Waterways Board to Devon County Council, together with £38,750 for maintenance - a sum based on the capitalised value of the cost of maintaining the canal in previous years. In addition to the potential interest from the capital sum it was clear that further finance would be needed for maintenance and running expenses, and contributions to provide this were agreed by the borough, rural district, and county councils.

Initial essential work involved the cutting of weed, and silt removal at the Tiverton end of the canal. The management body's main problem, that of the half-mile dry section at Halberton, was next to be tackled. Decision had already been taken that for ultimate success restoration of this section was vital, to ensure a continuous waterway, but the seriousness of the leaks due to fissured bedrock was a matter of much concern. This was dealt with during the restoration work by the application of butyl plastic sheeting, covered for protection with a coat of clay. Once completed, water from the eastern end of the canal could again flow to Tiverton, and before long nature restored the scene with plant growth and other wildlife. Meanwhile, fishing and boating by small unpowered craft were becoming increasingly possible, although this was discouraged on the $2^1/_2$-mile eastern end from Fossend to Lowdwells, which was designated as a nature reserve.

On 13 July 1974 completion of the initial restoration work was marked by an official festive occasion which included inauguration of a new horseboat service. After ceremonies at Tiverton basin the boat set off on a cruise along the canal to Sampford Peverell, carrying a party of councillors, officials and guests. Soon the canal was attracting people from all over the south-west, often coming in groups to enjoy a day out. And completion of the M5 motorway in 1977 brought increasing numbers of visitors from afar into the region, many of whom found the quiet leisured progress of the horseboat a welcome antidote to driving on busy roads.

Helen Harris launching *The Tivertonian* in July 1974. *(Tiverton Gazette)*

Further operations involving the canal have been necessary since that time, including some to deal with urgent matters. The long familiar problem of the leaks west of Halberton, between Greenway Bridge and Tiverton Road Bridge, flared again as the polythene membrane laid in1973, which had served reasonably well, showed signs of wear and tear, with frequently occurring leakage. In 1987 the canal's water level fell severely, for which running repairs were inadequate. A further sense of crisis developed and financial options considered – even, once again, that of abandonment, but this, it was shown, would actually be more costly than maintenance. Following a contractors' report of 1990, major works were put in hand immediately, including a relining of the leaking section with high-density polyethylene. Other leaks, west of Fenacre Bridge, were repaired in 1992, and smaller ones in the aqueduct over the disused Tiverton branch railway were eliminated by some rebuilding and relining with sprayed concrete. Constant attention has to be paid by maintenance staff to sedimentation and invasive aquatic vegetation as well as to the upkeep of towpath, hedges and gates.

Various works have been carried out along the canal over the years for the benefit of the visiting public, but always in accordance with its designation as a Local Nature Reserve. Owned by Devon County Council and managed in partnership with Mid Devon District Council, management on the ground is in the hands of the Grand Western Canal Country Park Ranger Service. Improvements at and around Tiverton basin have included restoration of limekilns, provision of parking, picnic areas and lavatories, and in 2013 a new visitor centre. Besides the horse-drawn barge there are a floating cafe, tea rooms and gardens, and a gift shop. Boating facilities have been expanded, with the construction of a slipway near Sampford Peverell in 2003, allowing visiting boats to launch under

Remains of the Nynehead lift after clearance and restorations work (2013).

The aqueduct near Nynehead which carried the canal over the River Tone (2013).

The iron trough of the aqueduct which carried the canal over the River Tone (2013).

Looking down, eastwards, from the top of the Nynehead lift (2013).

permit. The horse-drawn service continues to be popular, run by Tiverton Canal Company, enabling visitors to experience a countryside 'voyage' on the only horse-drawn barge still operating in the westcountry. The Tiverton Canal Company also provides motorised day boats, rowing boats and Canadian canoes for hire. Cycle hire is available at Abbotshead Farm beside Greenway Bridge in Halberton.

Three new bridges have been constructed over the canal in recent times, two of them memorials – a footbridge just beyond the basin, and another at Tiverton Road Bridge – and a substantial one beyond Sampford Peverell which carries the North Devon link road (A361) from the M5. Restoration of many of the earlier features, including wharves and the group of limekilns at the Waytown end, have been carried out. The canal can be accessed at various points along the route,and fishing continues to be a popular recreation.

For many people – in Devon, Somerset and beyond – the Grand Western Canal holds great interest, for its history, surviving structures, and archaeology. In 1988 the Grand Western Canal Trust was formed to promote use and enjoyment of the waterway, and in 1997 the Trust was incorporated as the Grand Western Canal Association Limited and registered as a charity. It is thus eligible to apply for funds from various bodies in respect of suitable projects, the main object being to promote and assist in the renovating, conservation and best long-term maintenance of all sections of the Grand Western route between Tiverton in Devon and Taunton in Somerset. The Trust was re- branded as the Friends of the Grand Western Canal in 2012, emphasising its valued function as a support group.

Work has been carried out at various points from Lowdwells eastwards in clearing and restoring features on the long-abandoned length to Taunton. This has been done by members of the Trust, greatly aided by volunteers and parties from such bodies as the Waterways Recovery Group of the Inland Waterways Association. One of the earlier stretches tackled was in an area known as Jay's Cutting, near Cothay Manor, where clearance work and re-watering has proceeded in stages. In various places, with the interest of landowners, other attempts have been made to bring to light evidence of the waterway. Between the foot of the Wellisford inclined plane and Harpford Bridge the area of Rewe Mead has been purchased by Somerset Wildlife Trust and is managed by it, partly as clear water and the remainder as wildlife habitat.

The Nynehead lift has been a major scene of activity, largely due to the initiative and energy of Denis Dodd and his wife Jenny (who sadly died in 2006), by whom the property on which it stands was bought in 1997. This lift, of all the seven, is the only one showing truly recognisable features, and Mr Dodd, with others including the IWA rescue group, Somerset Industrial Archaeology Society and further voluntary bodies, has done much to clear, excavate and interpret surviving structures in work backed by documentary research. During the process a local contractor was engaged and the lift chamber and associated lock cleared of silt. A 100-metre stretch of the lower level approach to the lift has been cleared, dredged and re-watered, and the towpath made accessible. Excavations have also exposed remains of a lift-keeper's cottage. Restoration of the lift and of the aqueduct which carried the canal across the old carriageway to Nynehead Court was intensified in 2011, with the involvement of scaffolding and the employment of professional building skills. Voluntary funding has been assisted by some much appreciated grants. The input of Somerset County Council and English Heritage for support and DEFRA / Natural England for funding at Nynehead have been greatly valued.

Some voluntary clearance and preservation work has also been done on the aqueduct which carried the canal across the River Tone, but this, as with similar attentions to the Lowdwells lock, is being held in abeyance for the time. Nearer to Taunton, the former Silk Mill Bridge, by which the old Bishop's Hull – Staplegrove road crossed the waterway, has been swept away in the course of road improvements. Beyond this, as Taunton Railway Station is approached, signs of the canal have disappeared completely in the complex of rail lines and other developments.

The present aim, backed by Somerset County Council, is to make as much as possible of the former canal route available to walkers and to preserve and protect the canal's features wherever feasible.

The autumn of 2012 was a season of exceptionally high rainfall in south-west England. For the Grand Western Canal this reached a disastrous peak on the night of 20-21 November, when over two inches of rain fell on already saturated ground and the canal was swollen by flooding with which overflow arrangements could not cope. In several places the banks overtopped, and on the afternoon of the 21st the Halberton embankment, west of Rock Bridge (which had caused engineer John Rennie concern in 1813) gave way. Erosion and rapid collapse caused a huge breach and water poured out on to the adjacent land – fortunately on the north side, otherwise Halberton village would have been inundated.

Devon County Council Country Park Manager Mark Baker and his staff were already aware of the critically developing situation and just two hours before had installed stop boards at Rock Bridge and Greenway Bridge which helped retard the westward flow, enabling barriers to be placed when the collapse came. As soon as this occurred action accelerated. Pumps were brought in and the canal to east and west securely stanked off, with many local people, and Friends of the GW Canal, coming in to help. Thanks to quick attentions the emergency was soon contained and the structure temporarily stabilised.

The sight of the gaping breach and exposure of bright red Devon soil was a sad one. But determination to seek restoration was apparent and immediate. Within days the Friends' chairman, Robert Hodgson, announced the opening of a Rescue Fund which drew generous response from subscriptions and varied ideas for raising money. Clearly, substantial sums would be needed for funding complete reconstruction and great was the relief when, early in 2013, an announcement from the canal's owner, Devon County Council, indicated that DCC would cover the full cost. (The Rescue Fund could then be used variously to sustain the canal's future viability). It was made clear that the huge response to the Friends' appeal, which indicated the cherished status of the canal for local people, besides its historical and amenity value to Devon, had been important factors in DCC's decision.

In July 2013 DCC announced its appointment of South West Highways Ltd as contractor, with work to commence forthwith. Eroded embankment material which had settled could be recovered for restructuring. The canal would be lined over the 360-metre length of the embankment with impervious material which would be covered and hidden. Other repairs and modifications would also be carried out. As work proceeded it was

The breach of 2012. *(Nigel Cuthbert)*

View of the breach after waters receded, April 2013.

found that, because of unforeseen unstable erosive conditions, further supportive measures would be needed, and it was further decided to provide a concrete channel over a 20-metre stretch beside Swing Bridge. Other works, including some repairs of wharves and bridges, and provision of remote monitoring of water levels and an alarm system, and further stop-boards, were also undertaken. Over the coming years further improvements including new sluices and weirs, will be made, providing greater capacity to release water and avoid overtopping in severe weather conditions.

The additional work, plus delays due to unfavourable weather conditions, will involve extra time, and cost. But it is still hoped that the restoration will be complete and the waterway in full use again in time for celebrations to mark the 200th anniversary of the canal's opening, planned for May 2014.

And so, the Grand Western Canal, topic of discussion for more than two centuries, after a troubled working existence and idleness for over 50 years, has gone forward into new life, with amenities that bring pleasure to many people. Perhaps the hoped-for profits, which never materialised financially for the subscribers in the early days, may be reaped increasingly by their successors in the form of recreation and enjoyment, which, in the new age of leisure, the canal has the potential to provide.

A modern-day scene at the Tiverton basin. *(Philip Brind)*

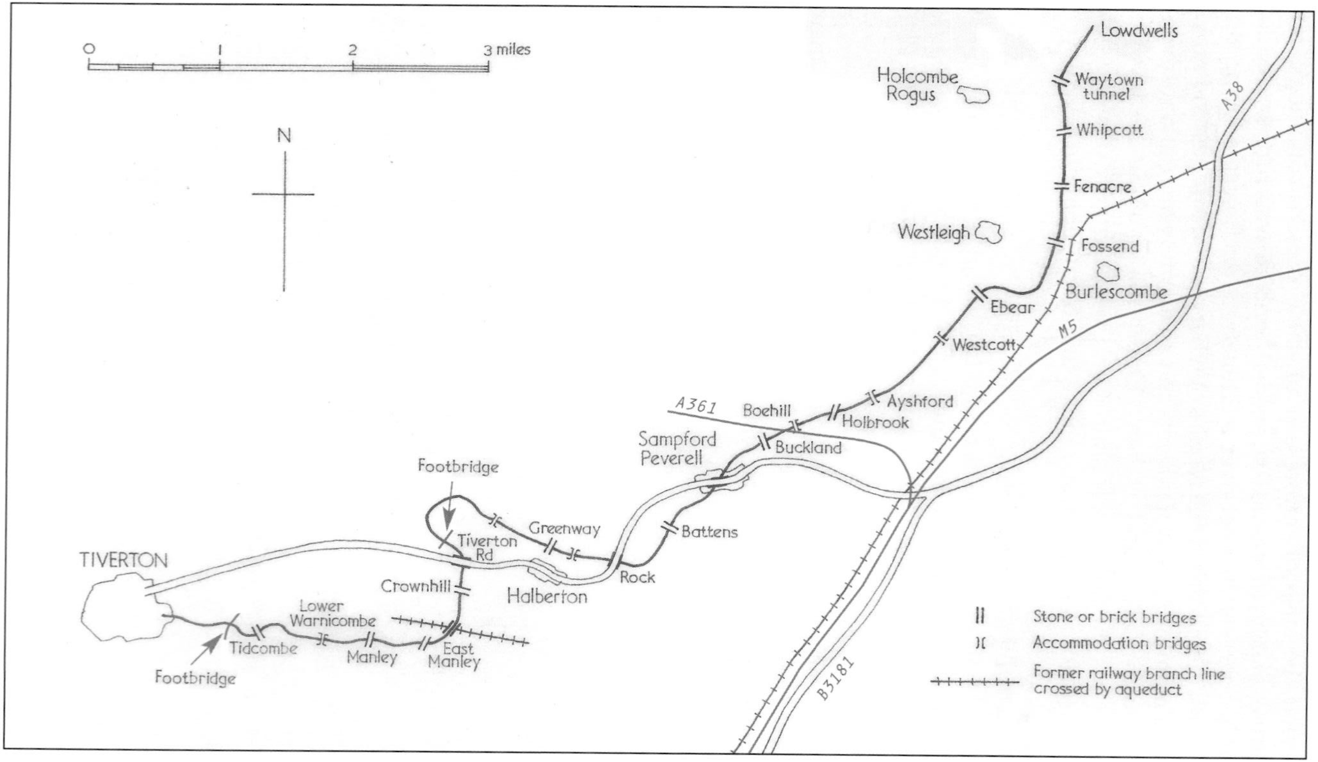

The Grand Western Canal, Tiverton-Lowdwells.

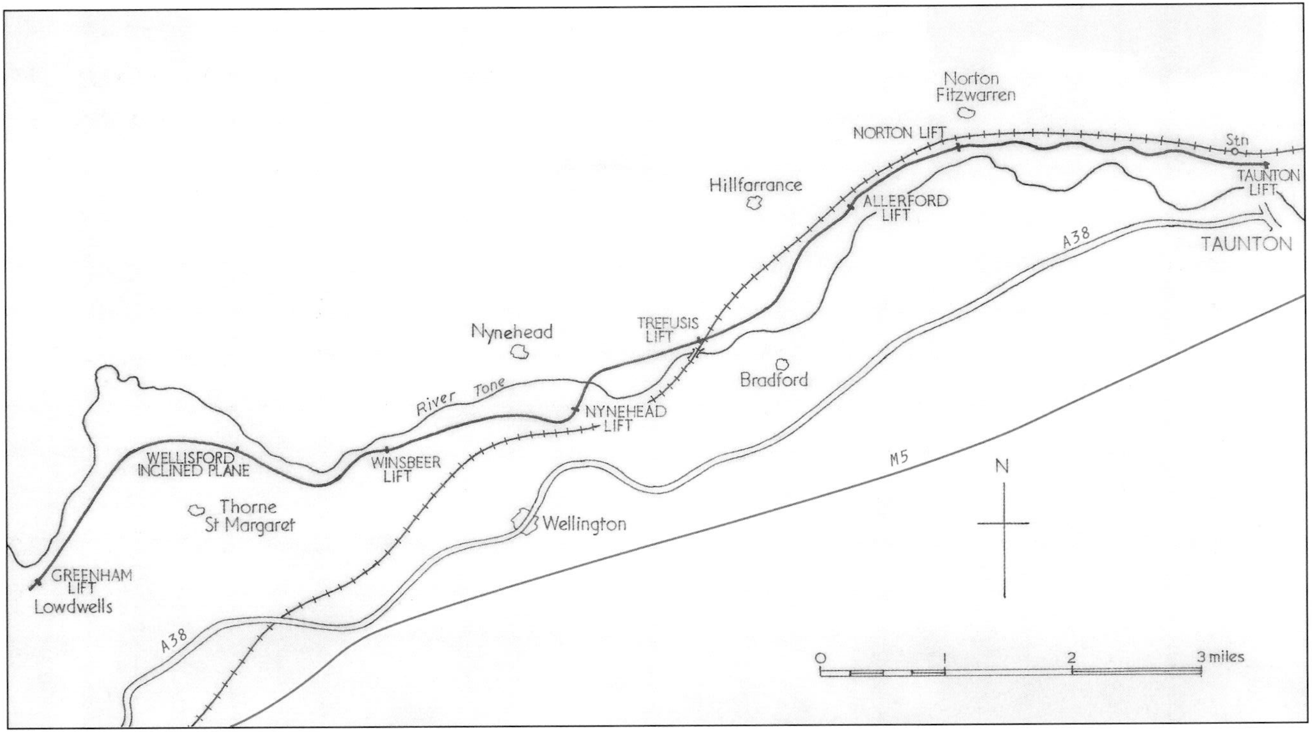

The route of the abandoned Taunton-Lowdwells length of the Grand Western Canal, showing positions of lifts and inclined plane.

Index